Note to Parents\Teachers

I had the idea for this book because I've always been
a keen swimmer and hoped that my own children
would be able to enjoy swimming, too.
Their disabilities meant that some specialist help
and instruction was needed for them to be able
to access their lessons, but with the right help and support
they became as confident in the water as any other child.
Sue Bordley

During my 13 years as a lifeguard and swimming teacher
I've loved helping children learn to swim and enjoy being
in the water, and of course safety plays a huge part in that.
I wanted this book to provide an easy to understand guide
for children of all abilities that would enable everyone
to have fun and be safe.
Jonathan Gerrard RLSS Lifeguard.
Swim England Level 1 & 2 and Baby and Pre-School level 1 & 2.

This book is intended to show parents, siblings and friends how
they can help a person with disabilities enjoy being in the water,
as well as provide information about water safety for all children.

Meet Lifeguard Rob and Lifeguard Jen.

They work at the swimming pool.

They keep everyone safe.

They also teach children to swim.

As the pool was about to open, Jen said,

"I'm looking forward to another great day

of people having fun in the pool."

"Me too," Rob replied.

"I love keeping everyone safe

when they come swimming."

Today was school swimming lessons day.

Sam was especially keen to get into the water

and started running towards the edge of the pool.

The floor was wet and he slipped!

Rob helped Sam up. Luckily, he wasn't hurt.

"I'm glad you're okay, Sam," he said,

"but I hope you understand now why you

shouldn't run at the poolside."

"Yes, I do," said a slightly-sore Sam.

 What should you do at the side of the pool?

The children lined up to see Jen,

who gave them all armbands.

"Now we've got our armbands on," she said,

"we can get started.

Line up at the shallow end, please."

"What does shallow end mean?" asked Keira.

Rob said, "The shallow end is the end you can

stand up in. That's where we're going to start.

Until you're a good swimmer, you should only go

to the deep end if an adult or your swimming

teacher is helping you."

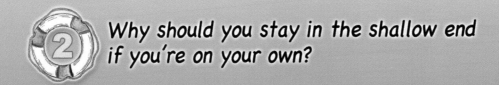

Why should you stay in the shallow end
if you're on your own?

"Right everyone, sit at the side of the pool.
I want you to listen," Jen told the children.
They all sat at the edge of the shallow end,
dipping their feet in the water.
"Swimming can be lots of fun, but it's
very important to be safe."
"Yes," Rob agreed.
"We're going to tell you some pool safety rules."
However, Sam wasn't listening. He was fiddling
with his armband and wiggling his feet in the
water, making a whooshing noise.
"Keep your feet still, please, Sam," Jen said.
"I need everyone to be able to hear what I'm saying."
"Sorry," he answered. "I'll keep still now."

 Why do you need to pay attention when your swimming teacher is explaining the rules?

Rob and Jen gave out some floats.

"We're going to do leg-kicks now," Rob said. "Listen carefully. Put your feet flat against the wall of the pool. Then push off as hard as you can, holding the float out at the same time, then move yourself forward by kicking your legs. Your target is five metres, which is halfway across the pool. Let's see who can do it!"

The children did as he said. Their feet made a lot of noise as they kicked and splashed their way to the middle. Keira got there first, but Tyler struggled to kick the right way.

"Good job, Keira!" Jen said. "Great kicking! And good effort, Tyler! We're going to practise kicking until everyone's got it. Keep trying!"

"I'm not going to give up," Tyler said. "I'm going to keep trying until I get better."

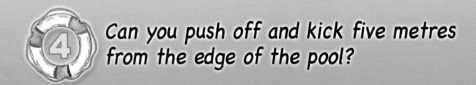

④ Can you push off and kick five metres from the edge of the pool?

"We're going to do floating next," Rob said.

"Watch what I'm doing."

Rob showed the children how they could float in the water, like starfish!

"Keep completely still. I know you think you'll sink, but you won't as long as you don't move," Jen told the class.

"Your armbands will help you, too."

Tyler held his arms and legs out straight.

His toes peeped out of the water.

"Look Jen, I'm doing it, I'm floating!"

"You're a star, Tyler!" the lifeguards said.

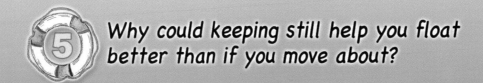

5 *Why could keeping still help you float better than if you move about?*

The class played waterball. It was lots of fun. Katie slipped when she was trying to run in the water, but her armbands kept her afloat. At one point, she tried to put her feet on the floor, but she'd gone too far and was in the deep end! "Jen! What should I do?" she cried.

"Don't panic, Katie. Move to the edge, grab the ledge and pull yourself back until you can put your feet on the floor." Katie joined the other children and the game continued.

"Running in water isn't easy!" she laughed. "Oops, I nearly bumped into you, Tyler."

With a smile, Tyler said, "I won't get too close to you in case you slip again, Katie."

"Well done, Tyler," the lifeguards said. "Always make sure there's space between you and other people in the pool."

 Why should you make sure you have plenty of space when you're in a swimming pool?

When the children were dressed, it was time to go back to school.

"See you next week," the lifeguards said, waving. "Hope you've had a good time."

Before they left, Sam approached Jen.

"Sorry I didn't listen, Jen," he said. "I know I should have, but I find it hard to concentrate."

"Thanks," Jen said, "but please make sure you try extra hard next week."

"I've got a sister," he went on. "We're coming swimming on Saturday, but I'm worried about her. She gets extra help at school, you see. She can't hear very well and she's got some other problems."

"Rob and I will be here on Saturday. We'd love to help her."

WATCH

On Saturday, Rob and Jen were watching the pool as usual, making sure everyone was safe. Jen saw Sam coming out of the changing area. She guessed the girl with him was his sister. He was holding her arm. She looked worried.

Jen walked over to them, before crouching down so that Chloe could see her face. She spoke in short sentences. "Hello, I'm Jen. I'm a lifeguard. I can help you. Would you like that?"

Chloe nodded and smiled.

"Watch me, and I'll show you what to do," Jen said.

"Thanks," her mum said. "I want Chloe to learn to swim, just like Sam."

ON THE SIDE

Jen moved to the part of the pool where there were not many people. She made a sign with her hands. Chloe understood and sat by the side of the pool.

Kneeling beside her, Jen told Chloe how to kick off from the side of the pool, holding a float.

"Okay, Chloe, so how are you going to do it?"

"I'm going to bend my knees, then hold my arms out," she said.

"That's right!" Jen said, giving her a 'Well done' signal.

WELL DONE

Rob fetched some rubber ducks from the store cupboard. He tossed two into the water, where they floated into the middle of the pool. He also knelt down so that Chloe could see him speak.

He pointed to the ducks. "Can you see those ducks? I want you to push off from the side of the pool, then move your arms like this." Rob showed how the children needed to keep their fingers together and sweep the water aside with their arms.

"Do you think you can catch those ducks?"

"Yeah!" Sam and Chloe said together.

FRONT CRAWL

Sam pushed off quickly, but Chloe started to struggle. She couldn't remember what to do. Rob was at the side of the pool. He waved to get her attention. "Watch me, Chloe!" he said, as he showed her the arm movements again.

"Go on, get that duck!" A few seconds later, Sam was swimming back to the side of the pool with his duck, and Chloe reached out to grab hers.

"Good job, both of you!" Rob said, really pleased with them.

WATCH

WELL DONE

Rob brought out three noodles. He gave the children one each, and used the other to show the children how they could be seahorses! "Lift your legs up, and the noodle will keep you afloat," he told them. Sam and Chloe did so. "No, I'm sinking!" she cried out. "I'm scared!" Jen signalled to get Chloe's attention again. "It's okay, Chloe, just kick your legs and wave your hands like this," she reassured her. Chloe did what Jen had said. Within seconds, she was floating. She laughed. "This is fun," she said. "I love swimming!" When it was time to go home, Mum said, "Thank you so much for helping Chloe. I want her to be able to do everything Sam does." Jen and Rob smiled. "We're glad she had a good time. We want everyone to enjoy swimming. We'll be here to help her next time, and Sam knows how to help her now, too."

STOP

GET CHANGED

Are you a swimming superstar?

Check out the answers to our quiz questions!

 You should always walk at the side of a swimming pool, so you don't slip and fall like Sam!

 You should stay in the shallow end (where you can touch the floor with your feet) so you don't get out of your depth and stuck in deep water.

 You should always pay attention while your swimming teacher is explaining the rules to make sure everyone can hear their instructions.

 If you can push off and kick for 5 metres, that's amazing! Keep trying until you can do it!

 If you wave your arms and legs around in the water, it stops you floating. Try to keep as still as you can, and after a few seconds you should start to float.

 You need space around you in the pool to stop you bumping into other people.

How many did you get right?

Goodbye for now!

We hope you've enjoyed learning how
to have fun and be safe in the water.

See you at the pool again soon!